A KINGDOM LOST FOR A DROP OF HONEY

And Other Burmese Folktales

By Maung Htin Aung and Helen G. Trager

Illustrated by Paw Oo Thet

PARENTS' MAGAZINE PRESS · NEW YORK

Book Designed by Mildred Kantrowitz

CONTENTS

FOREWORD

THE SMALL southeast Asian country of Burma, half a world away, is little known to Americans. These fifteen folktales are offered by way of a pleasant introduction.

There are fifteen folktales for several reasons, but one is because fifteen is a typical Burmese sum. The Burmese people reckon not by dozens but by tens, and factors or multiples of ten. They use the decimal system with consistency. Things are counted or grouped in sets of 5's, 10's, 15's etc., whether it is hen's eggs, teacups or tennis balls.

A nation's folktales can tell you a lot about a country and the people. I think that Burmese folktales do. Though no two of these tales are very much alike, they reveal qualities that many Burmese people have: a directness, almost bluntness, yet restraint and courtesy. Also, you come on unexpected things, like surprise endings and surprise characters. You don't expect Mr. Industry to be a failure and Mr. Luck to win the hand of the Princess, but that happens. It wouldn't come as a surprise to you if you were Burmese, however. Nor, if you were Burmese, would you be surprised to read that Master Thumb's staunch friend is the Rain, and his mortal enemy is the Sun.

Only some of these tales are funny, like "The Four Deaf Men," or "The Drunkard and the Opium-Eater." But many of them have humor. If humor were lacking these wouldn't be Burmese tales, for Burmese people enjoy laughter. They have a keen sense of the ridiculous; they delight in preposterous, incongruous situations, and are able to laugh at themselves. They enjoy broad slapstick and quiet humor, as in "The Case of the Calf and the Colt," and the little opening tale, "The Greedy Stallkeeper and the Poor Traveler."

A type of tale included here in several variations is one in which there is discord or argument. The Burmese way of coping with conflict in real life is essentially as the folktales portray it. The parties in a dispute voluntarily seek out an individual with a cool heart and a wise head; in the folktales, it is the wise rabbit, the village headman or the Princess Learned-in-the-Law. True to Burmese Buddhist tradition, their decisions must be directed at the reestablishment of harmony, rather than at establishing guilt or meting out punishment. And the individuals who brought the dispute to the

12

arbiter must go away feeling satisfied, as in "Partnership" and "The Bee-Hunter and the *Oozie*."

The tales in this collection come from the area around Mandalay in Central Burma. They were selected expressly for young readers and are being published for the first time in the United States. These tales appear among several hundred others in two of Dr. Htin Aung's scholarly books: *Burmese Folk Tales* and *Burmese Law Tales*, Oxford University Press, London.

Helen G. Trager

Salem Center, New York
September, 1967

THE GREEDY STALLKEEPER AND THE POOR TRAVELER

A POOR TRAVELER stopped under a tree to eat his simple meal, which he had brought with him in a bundle. The meal consisted only of some cooked rice and boiled vegetables. It was the cool season, during which people traveled from one village to another, and there were many wayside stalls selling fried fish and fried cakes.

A few yards away to the north of the poor traveler, there was a food stall where the owner was frying some fish. She carefully watched the traveler as he ate his meal, and when he had finished, she called out, "Give me a silver coin for the fried fish."

"But, mistress," protested the poor traveler, "I have not even come near your stall, let alone taken some fish from you."

"You miser! You cheat!" shouted the stallkeeper. "Everybody can see that you have been enjoying your meal with the fragrant smell of my fried fish. Without the smell, your meal of rice and salt could not have been so tasty."

A crowd soon collected, and although their sympathy was with the poor traveler, all had to admit that as the wind was blowing from the north, it must have carried the aroma from the frying pan to the traveler.

Finally, the woman and the traveler, unable to settle their dispute, went before the Princess Learned-in-the-Law, and she passed the following judgment:

"The stallkeeper insists that the traveler ate his meal with the smell of her fried fish. The traveler cannot deny that the wind did carry the smell of frying fish to his nostrils as he sat eating. Therefore, he must pay the price. But what was the price of fried fish? The woman says it is fixed at a silver coin for each plate of fried fish. Let the woman and the traveler go out of the court into the sunlight; let the traveler hold out a silver coin, and let the woman take the shadow cast by it. For if the price of a plate of fried fish is a silver coin, the price of the *smell* of a plate of fried fish must be the *shadow* of a silver coin."

MISTER LUCK AND MISTER INDUSTRY

MISTER LUCK and Mister Industry belonged to the same village, but they were very different in temperament. Mister Luck was not fond of work and he was a great believer in luck, whereas Mister Industry spent his time working and had no faith in luck. Mister Luck stayed at home, whereas Mister Industry went up the Irrawaddy River regularly, bringing down bamboo rafts. As the bamboo fetched high prices in his own district, Mister Industry was rich and owned a lot of cattle.

One day Mister Luck's parents scolded him for being a lazy fellow, and they ordered him to go along with Mister Industry as a raftsman. Mister Luck told all his friends that it was his luck which was forcing him to go and that he was certain the journey up the Irrawaddy would be very lucky for him.

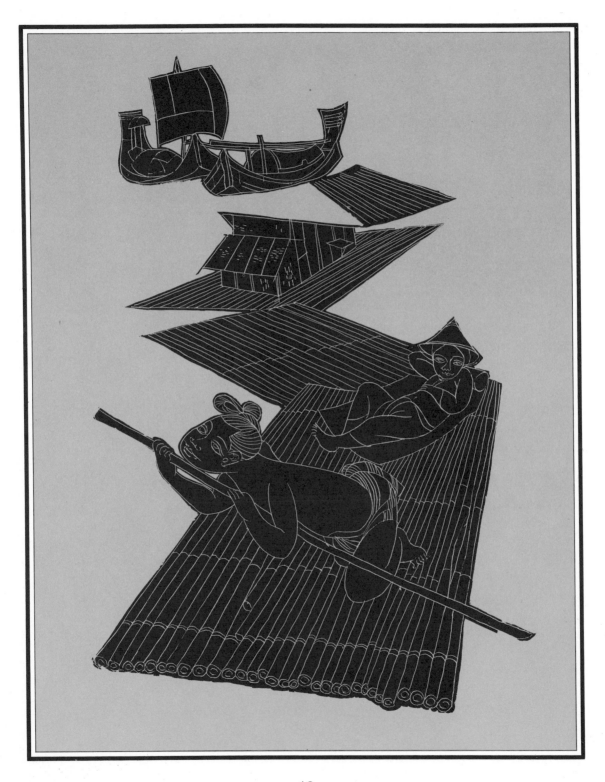

On the outward journey Mister Luck met with no fortunate incident, and Mister Industry jeered at him. "Well, where is that piece of great luck which you expected to find on your journey?"

"Wait," said Mister Luck. "Luck comes slowly but surely."

On the return journey a great storm arose, and the bamboo rafts had to be moored to the shore at once. The place where they stopped was wild and desolate, and Mister Industry taunted Mister Luck. "Well, is this the piece of great luck which you expected to find on your journey?" The other raftsmen laughed.

Mister Luck, getting bored with their sneers and jeers, went for a stroll on the riverbank. "We won't wait for you if you are too long!" shouted Mister Industry.

"If my luck wills that I should be left behind," replied Mister Luck, "I will not complain." He walked on and came to a pool

of water as clear as crystal. Wanting to bathe in the clear water, he jumped into the pool; at once he was changed into a monkey. But he did not complain. "If my luck wills that I should end my days as a monkey, I am satisfied," he said to himself.

He walked on a few yards and came to a pool of muddy water. "Might as well try this also," he said, and jumped into the pool; at once he became a human being again. Finding two water jars nearby, he filled one with the crystal-clear water and the other with the muddy water. Then he returned with the two water jars to the rafts, which were still moored as the storm had not yet abated.

"What luck?" asked Mister Industry. "What have you there?"

"Only water," replied Mister Luck.

"A wonderful gift from your luck!" jeered Mister Industry. "A gift of water for a raftsman on the Irrawaddy."

Mister Luck made no reply. The storm had now abated, and the men steered the rafts on down the river.

They moored the rafts at Prome, a royal city along their route, and Mister Industry went ashore to see some bamboo merchants. Mister Luck sat on his raft, idly watching a water seller having a swim after filling his water jars. Mister Luck had an idea and, taking his jar of crystal-clear water, he went toward the water jars. He then chose one at random and, after half-emptying it, he poured in the crystal-clear water. "Now let us see who is lucky enough or unlucky enough to use this water for a bath," laughed Mister Luck.

The water seller came and took away his water jars to hawk

them around the city. Now the king of Prome had a beautiful
daughter, and it so happened that on that particular morning there
was not enough water in her bath because her maidservants had
neglected to fill it. The princess was very angry, and a maidservant
rushed out to fetch some water. Meeting the water seller, she bought
a jar from him to save the time of going to the river. The jar she
bought was the one into which Mister Luck had poured the crystal-
clear water. No wonder the princess turned into a monkey the
moment she took her bath!

The king sent his gongsmen all over the city to announce that the princess had been transformed into a monkey by witchcraft, and that any wizard who could cure her would be given her hand in marriage. Mister Luck heard the news and went to the palace with his jar of muddy water. He sprinkled the water on the princess and at once she became a human being. Mister Luck married the princess and became crown prince. Later the king died, and so Mister Luck became king.

One monsoon, misfortune befell Mister Industry. All his rafts foundered in a storm, all his money was stolen, and all his cattle died except one old cow. "My old raftsman, Mister Luck, is now a king," he thought to himself. "If I take this cow to him and say that it is all I now possess, he will surely give me gold and jewels out of pity." So he went to the palace with the old cow.

The palace guard stopped him at the gates and inquired what was his business with the king. Mister Industry lost his nerve at the sight of the gleaming swords of the palace guards, and he did not know what to say. One of the guards gave a prod with his sword and repeated the question, "Come, what is your business with the king?" At this, becoming more embarrassed, he ran away, leaving his cow with the guards. And so Mister Industry became a pauper.

WHY THE RABBIT'S NOSE TWITCHES

THE FROG was jealous of the rabbit's reputation for wisdom, and planned to make the rabbit the laughingstock of the animal kingdom. So he hid himself underneath a stone and when he saw the rabbit coming along leisurely, the frog shouted in a loud voice *"Ong-Jng!"*

The rabbit jumped one cubit into the air and then ran away in fright. As he ran, he knocked down a pumpkin. The pumpkin rolled down the slope to a field and bumped against a sesamum plant, scattering the seeds. A *yit*, or wild pheasant, happened to be flying over the spot, and some of the seeds got into his eyes, temporarily

blinding him. The *yit* alighted on a bamboo plant. The bamboo broke and fell on a snake who was sleeping underneath. The snake ran away in fright and bumped against the wild pig who was quietly eating a cucumber. The wild pig dropped it in fright, and the cucumber fell into the nearby pool. There was a *Naga* dragon sleeping at the bottom of the pool, and he felt annoyed at being disturbed by the cucumber.

"You shall die," said the *Naga* to the cucumber.

"Oh, sir, oh, sir," replied the cucumber, "I am not to blame. The wild pig pushed me in."

The *Naga* left the pool and soon caught the pig. "You shall die," said the *Naga*.

"Oh, sir, oh, sir," replied the pig, "I am not to blame. The snake bumped against me."

The *Naga* chased the snake and soon caught him. "You shall die," said the *Naga*.

"Oh, sir, oh, sir," replied the snake, "I am not to blame. The bamboo fell on me."

The *Naga* went to the bamboo and said, "You shall die."

"Oh, sir, oh, sir," replied the bamboo, "I am not to blame. The wild pheasant alighted on me."

The *Naga* soon caught the wild pheasant and said, "You shall die."

"Oh, sir, oh, sir," replied the wild pheasant, "the sesamum plant threw his seeds into my eyes and blinded me."

The *Naga* went to the sesamum plant and said, "You shall die."

"Oh, sir, oh, sir," replied the sesamum plant, "I am not to blame. The pumpkin bumped into me."

The *Naga* soon found the pumpkin and said, "You shall die."

"Oh, sir, oh, sir," replied the pumpkin, "the rabbit knocked me down."

The *Naga* found the rabbit and said, "You shall die."

"Oh, sir, oh, sir," replied the rabbit, "I am not to blame. A monster from under a stone frightened me."

The *Naga* went and looked under the stone, but as the frog had fled, he could not find anything under the stone. The *Naga* went back to the rabbit, and said, "You little liar, there was no monster, and you shall die."

The poor rabbit stood there trembling with fright. Then his nose began to twitch. It twitched and twitched and twitched. The *Naga* roared with laughter to see the rabbit's nose twitching. His temper now recovered, he went back to his pool. And even to the present day, the rabbit's nose is forever twitching.

A KINGDOM LOST FOR A DROP OF HONEY

THE KING and his chief minister were in a merry mood as they stood by the palace window, eating roasted rice and honey. They laughed so much that they spilled some honey on the windowsill.

"We have spilled some honey, Your Majesty," said the chief minister. "Let me wipe it off."

"My dear Lord," laughed the king, "it is beneath your dignity to do it, and if we call a servant to wipe it away, he will disturb our pleasant conversation. So let the spilt honey alone."

They went on eating and laughing while a drop of honey trickled down the windowsill onto the street below.

"Chief Minister," said the king, leaning forward, "a drop of the honey has fallen on the street and a fly is now feasting on it."

The chief minster looked and saw a spider pouncing on the fly. The king looked down again and saw the spider caught and swallowed by a house lizard. Amused, the king continued to eat and laugh with the minister and soon they saw the lizard eaten up by a cat.

When a dog appeared on the scene and began to attack the cat, they went on laughing and eating and they did not pause even when they saw the owner of the cat and the owner of the dog quarreling and fighting.

Soon friends of both parties joined in the fight. Still the king and his minister continued to make merry. The fighting now spread to other streets and only then did the king and the chief minster shout out orders to the palace guards to quell the fighting. However, by that time, the palace guards themselves had joined the fray, as some of them supported the owner of the dog while others supported the owner of the cat.

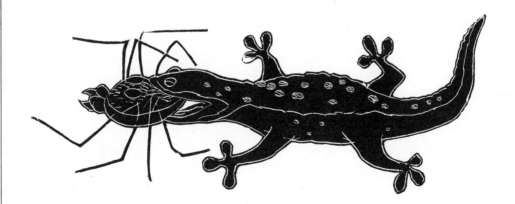

Within the next few hours, civil war had broken out, the city burned and the palace destroyed together with the king and the chief minister.

A group of judges went to the Princess Learned-in-the-Law and asked for her advice and counsel. She gave thought to what they asked and she said: "My Lord Justices, take note that there is no such thing as a minor incident, and judges must not delay but deal with each swiftly and promptly, no matter how trivial it may appear to be. Remember always, my Lords, the case of the kingdom which was lost because of a mere drop of honey."

THE FOUR DEAF MEN

ONCE THERE LIVED four deaf men in a village. The first was a herdsman, the second earned his living by climbing palm trees to extract toddy juice, the third was a farmer, and the fourth the headman of the village.

One morning the herdsman missed his cattle, which had strayed away during the night. He searched and searched but without success. Then he saw the toddy-climber up a palm tree and asked, "Have you seen my cattle?"

The toddy-climber, of course, could not hear him, but thought the herdsman was asking about the palms. "This tree is not so good," he said, and he pointed to a grove some distance away. "The trees over there are much better."

"Thank you," said the herdsman, thinking that the toddy-climber was telling him where to find the missing cattle. He went to the distant grove of palm trees, and actually he found his cattle there.

The herdsman was now hot and tired from searching for his cattle the whole morning, and he wanted to take the shortcut to his home. To do that, he had to go over the land belonging to the farmer. The herdsman found the farmer burning the meadow grass on his land and, pointing to his cattle, he said, "May I cross with my cattle?"

The farmer thought that the question was "Did you steal my cattle?" and he replied, "No, no," shaking his head vigorously.

"Now, now," said the herdsman, "why are you so mean? Your

land is not yet plowed, and surely my cattle cannot spoil it."

The farmer went on shaking his head, saying, "No, no." At last they came to blows and each dragged the other to the headman's house.

The headman that morning had had an unfortunate misunderstanding with his wife, which resulted in his soundly beating her. The wife in disgust left the house and went home to her mother. The herdsman and the farmer arrived; each sued the other for assault, and each pleaded his case with eloquent gestures.

But the headman shook his head, and waving his hands, he said, "Go away! Go away! It is no good pleading on her behalf. I will not have her back. Let her stay on with her mother."

The herdsman and the farmer, believing that both their suits had been dismissed, went quietly away.

THE FISHERMAN AND THE KING'S CHAMBERLAIN

ONCE THERE WAS A KING who would not eat any meal unless it included a dish of fried fish. One day, there blew such a great storm that fishermen could not catch any fish. The king would not eat his breakfast because there was no fried fish and he was annoyed. Lunchtime came, but there was no fish and the king became angry. Dinnertime approached, but still there was no prospect of fish, and the king was now desperate.

"Let it be announced by beat of gong and drum," ordered he, "that the fisherman who brings me but one single fish will be given any reward that he may name."

However, the storm continued to rage, and the waters remained turbulent. At last at dusk, a fisherman, using a mere line and hook, caught a nice fat and oily fish, and he ran with all his might to the king's palace.

The guards, seeing the fish in the fisherman's hand, threw open the gates and passed the word that the fisherman was to be allowed to reach the king's chamber without hindrance. But at the chamber door, the chamberlain said, "Promise me half your reward and I will let you in."

"One-tenth," bargained the fisherman.

"Oh, no," said the chamberlain. "One-half, and no less."

"Agreed," replied the fisherman, and in great glee, the chamberlain announced to the king the arrival of a fish.

The king, in great joy, seized the fish from the fisherman's hand and rushed into the kitchen.

After the fish had been fried, the dinner laid before the king, and the king had eaten, he sat back hugging his well-filled stomach and said, "Fisherman, name your reward. Do you want to have a priceless ruby, a well-paid post, or a pretty maid from the queen's bower?"

"No, sire, no, sire," replied the fisherman, falling on his knees, "I want twenty lashes with your cane."

"The poor fellow is flustered," mused the king, "and he does not know what he is saying." So he said gently to the fisherman, "My man, you mean twenty rubies, or twenty elephants or even twenty horses."

"No, sire, no, sire," replied the fisherman, "I want just twenty lashes with your cane."

"I am sorry," sighed the king, "but I must keep my promise and give you what you ask." So saying, he whispered to his servant to beat the fisherman lightly.

"No sire, no, sire," said the fisherman, "not so softly, sire. Please hit me hard."

The king, somewhat annoyed, ordered the servant to wield the cane with more vigor, but when the fisherman had been given ten lashes, to his astonishment, the man jumped away. "Did he hit you too hard?" the king inquired with concern and pity.

"No, sire, no, sire," explained the fisherman, "but the remaining ten lashes are your chamberlain's share."

The poor chamberlain now had to confess what he had done, but pleaded, "My Lord, I asked for a half share of his reward, not his punishment."

"But this is my reward, and not my punishment," argued the fisherman. The king sent for the Princess Learned-in-the-Law to come and decide the case.

"My Lord King," said the Princess Learned-in-the-Law, after she had arrived and listened to the two parties to the dispute, "the chamberlain and the fisherman were partners in a business, to wit, to supply a fish to the king, and they agreed to share. But, my Lord, in a partnership, the agreement to share does not mean that only the profits are to be shared. It means that gain and loss, income and expenditure, success and failure, reward and punishment are also to be shared."

The king accepted the judgment of the Princess, and gave the chamberlain ten good lashes with his cane. Then he said, "The partnership is now dissolved as the business has ended. As a consequence, however, I order that the chamberlain be dismissed for corruption and disloyalty, and the fisherman appointed chamberlain in his place."

PARTNERSHIP

AN OTTER and a jackal lived near a river, and after a while they decided to form a partnership. They agreed that they would pool all the food each was able to gather, and that they would share it equally at the end of the day.

On the first day of their partnership, the otter caught some shrimps and the jackal picked some bananas. The food was shared equally, and the partners were satisfied.

On the second day, the jackal gathered some bamboo shoots, but the otter had an off-day and could find nothing. Faithful to the agreement, the jackal shared the bamboo shoots with the otter.

On the third day, the jackal had no luck at all, but the otter went fishing and succeeded in catching a gudgeon. Now, as the otter was greedy, he announced, "I will cut the fish into four parts. I will take the head and the belly, and you can take the rest."

"Be fair," replied the jackal. "I shared the bamboo shoots equally with you yesterday."

"And I am sharing the fish equally with you, also," argued the otter. "You will get two pieces and I will get two pieces."

"But you intend to take the tastier parts," protested the jackal.

"Remember, it is I who caught the gudgeon," boasted the otter. And they argued for a long time, getting nowhere, until they agreed to ask the rabbit to help them settle their disagreement.

The wise rabbit listened patiently to the arguments presented by each one. Then, taking a sharp stone, he cut the fish right down the center from head to tail in two equal parts. "Now both of you shall have a piece of the fat belly," he explained, "and both of you shall have a piece of the tasteless tail."

The otter and the jackal went away quite satisfied, and they lived together in happy partnership for many days.

THE ORIGIN OF THE COCONUT

MANY HUNDREDS of years ago a raft with three people on it reached a city on the Burmese coast. The three strangers were taken before the king. In answer to the king's questions, the strangers said that they had been set adrift on a raft on the orders of the king of their own country across the sea, because they were found guilty of certain crimes.

One of the strangers was a thief, another a witch, and the third a mischief-maker who harmed people by his tittle-tattle.

The king gave a house and one thousand silver coins to the thief, and allowed him to settle in Burma. "He was a thief only because he was poor," explained the king, "and now that he is no longer poor, he will make a good subject."

To the witch, also, the king gave a house and a thousand silver coins and allowed her to settle in Burma. "She bewitched people merely out of jealousy," explained the king, "and she was jealous of others only because she was poor and unhappy. Now that she is rich, she will no longer be jealous of other people's happiness."

But the king ordered the mischief-maker to be executed at once. "For," said the king, "once a mischief-maker, always a mischief-maker." So the mischief-maker was taken to the place of execution and his head was cut off.

The next day one of the king's officers passed by the place, and to his surprise he found the head of the mischief-maker rolling about on the ground. He was the more surprised when the head of the mischief-maker opened its mouth and said repeatedly, "Tell your king to come and kneel to me here. Otherwise I will come and knock off his head."

The officer ran back to the palace and reported the matter. But nobody believed him, and the king was angry, thinking that the officer was trying to make fun of him.

"Your Majesty can send another person along with me," sug-

gested the officer, "and he will surely bear me out." So another officer was sent along with the first to the place of execution. When they reached there, however, the head lay still and remained silent.

The second officer made his report, and the king in anger ordered the first officer to be executed at once as a teller of lies. So the unfortunate man was taken back to the place of execution, and his head was cut off in the presence of his fellow officers.

When the execution was over, the head of the mischief-maker opened its mouth and said, "Ha, ha, I can still make mischief by my tittle-tattle although I am dead." The officers, realizing that gross injustice had been done to a colleague, now dead, reported what they had seen and heard, and the king was full of grief and remorse.

Realizing that the head of the mischief-maker would make further trouble by his tittle-tattle, the king ordered that a deep pit be dug and the head buried inside it. His orders were obeyed and the head was buried. But the next morning a strange tree was seen growing from that pit. The strange tree had even stranger fruit, which resembled the head of the mischief-maker.

The tree today is called the coconut tree. It was originally called *gon-bin*, which in Burmese means "mischief-maker tree." But during the course of centuries, the pronunciation of the name has deteriorated, and it came to be *on-bin* or coconut tree.

And if you shake a coconut and then put it against your ear, you will hear a gurgling noise. For, you see, although now a fruit, the head of the mischief-maker still wants to make tittle-tattle.

HOW MASTER THUMB DEFEATED THE SUN

ONCE A POOR WOMAN who was with child was trying to dry some paddy. But the moment she put out her basket of paddy the sun disappeared, and the moment she took in her basket thinking it was going to rain, the sun shone bright and clear again. This was repeated so many times that the woman lost her temper and abused the sun roundly. The sun in return laid upon her a curse, with the result that when her son was born he was no bigger than a man's thumb. The child was given the name of Master Thumb.

Master Thumb felt very unhappy because other children made fun of his small stature, and when he reached the age of sixteen years he demanded of his mother the true reason for his being no bigger than a thumb. When he learned that the sun's curse was the cause, he said, "Mother, make me a rice cake tomorrow, for I am going in search of the sun to fight him."

Early next morning Master Thumb set out northwards in his quest for the sun. He took with him the cake which was many times bigger than himself.

It was midsummer, the fields were bare of vegetation, and the whole countryside groaned under the intense heat. As he traveled on, Master Thumb met an old boat left high and dry. The stream on which it was floating had been dried up by the sun. "Master Thumb," greeted the boat, "where are you going?"

"I go to fight my enemy, the sun," was the reply.

Now the boat was also very bitter against the sun, for the sun had dried up his stream. So he pleaded, "Please let me follow you."

"All right," replied Master Thumb. "Eat a bit of my cake and get inside my stomach." The boat did as he was told.

Master Thumb traveled on, and he met a bamboo thorn. "Where are you going, Master Thumb?" greeted the bamboo thorn.

"I go to fight my enemy, the sun," was the reply.

Now the bamboo thorn also hated the sun, for the sun had caused all the bamboo plants to wither and fade. So he pleaded, "May I follow you?"

"All right," replied Master Thumb. "Eat a bit of my cake, and get inside my stomach." The bamboo thorn did as he was told.

Master Thumb traveled on, and he met a strip of moss. "Where are you going, Master Thumb?" greeted the moss.

"I go to fight my enemy, the sun," was the reply.

Now the moss also hated the sun, for the sun had dried up all the other moss nearby. And this moss had survived only because he had hidden himself among the roots of a big tree. So he pleaded, "May I come with you?"

"All right," replied Master Thumb. "Eat a bit of my cake, and get inside my stomach." The moss did as he was told.

Master Thumb traveled on, and he met a rotten egg. "Where are you going, Master Thumb?" greeted the rotten egg.

"I go to fight my enemy, the sun," was the reply.

Now the rotten egg also hated the sun, for his parents and relations, the fowls, had died of thirst as their streams were dried up by the sun. So he pleaded, "May I come with you?"

"All right," replied Master Thumb. "Eat a bit of my cake, and get inside my stomach." The rotten egg did as he was told.

So our Master Thumb, with his four faithful followers inside his stomach, traveled on, until at nightfall he reached the northern mountains, where he expected the sun to appear the next morning.

He decided to rest there for the night, and looked around for some shelter. To his surprise he saw a house some distance away. Master Thumb, being not only courageous but wise, realized that the house could not belong to a human being, but to an ogre. For only ogres live on bleak mountains and in wild forests. He walked to the house and decided that it was empty. "But the owner will come to sleep here for the night," said Master Thumb to himself, "and so I will wait and fight him for the house. I must have a good night's rest before my big battle."

At this moment the bamboo thorn, the moss, and the rotten egg jumped out of his stomach. "Master," they pleaded, "allow us to

fight the ogre, for you must reserve your strength for the morrow." Master Thumb reluctantly agreed and, hiding himself behind a bush, awaited events.

The three faithful followers entered the house, and the first thing they did was to hide the tinderbox. Then the bamboo thorn placed himself underneath the bed, the rotten egg in the kitchen fireplace, and the moss near the water jar.

Soon afterwards a big ogre came in and threw himself on the bed. The bamboo thorn gave him a series of sharp pricks. "Too many bugs in this bed," the ogre grumbled. "I must light my lamp and look for them."

He got up and felt for the tinderbox and, not finding it, he went to the kitchen to get a light. But as he bent over the fire the rotten egg burst its shell with a loud bang, scattering the ashes into the ogre's big eyes. The ogre groped his way to the water jar with the intention of washing out the cinders from his eyes, but he slipped on the moss and fell, breaking his neck. The three faithful servants reported the death of the ogre to Master Thumb and placed the house at his disposal.

At dawn Master Thumb, with his three faithful followers arrayed beside him, challenged the sun to come out and fight. The sun appeared, red with anger, and as he rose in the sky he made himself hotter and hotter until poor Master Thumb was nearly shriveled up by the heat. No doubt he would have been ignominiously destroyed had not an unexpected ally come to his aid. Now the rain had been fighting the sun since the beginning of time, and the

rain considered anyone who fought the sun worthy of his support. So the rain came down and quenched the sun.

Master Thumb and his three faithful followers laughed loudly at the sun's discomfort, but soon they became silent with dismay. For the rain, in quenching the sun, had caused great floods, and Master Thumb was now in danger of drowning.

At this juncture, however, out jumped the boat from inside Master Thumb's stomach and placed himself at his master's service. Master Thumb and his other three followers jumped into the boat and journeyed southwards together, back to Master Thumb's village. All the villagers came out with laughter and with shouts to greet the return of their hero, and to celebrate the defeat of the sun.

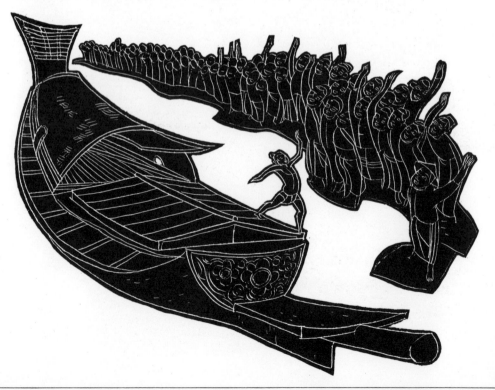

WHY THE TIGER IS SO ANGRY AT THE CAT

ALTHOUGH THE TIGER was big and strong and fierce, he was so clumsy in his movements that he became the laughingstock of the jungle. "Look at the clumsy tiger," the animals jeered. "He will soon starve to death because he is so clumsy that he cannot catch any prey."

The tiger felt very unhappy until he remembered his cousin, the cat. So he went to his cousin and said, "Cousin, please teach me all your methods of hunting and catching prey, and I will serve you faithfully for three full years." The cat agreed.

So the tiger became the pupil of the cat, and although they were cousins and he the elder, he showed the cat every respect due from a pupil to his teacher. He swept the house; he prepared the meals; he ran errands; he accompanied the cat wherever he went; and he learned his lessons. In short, the tiger was the perfect pupil. The cat at first was a good teacher but later he became jealous of his own pupil. "The tiger masters all the tricks I teach him," he reflected, "and if I teach all I know, he will rival me, nay, he will surpass me,

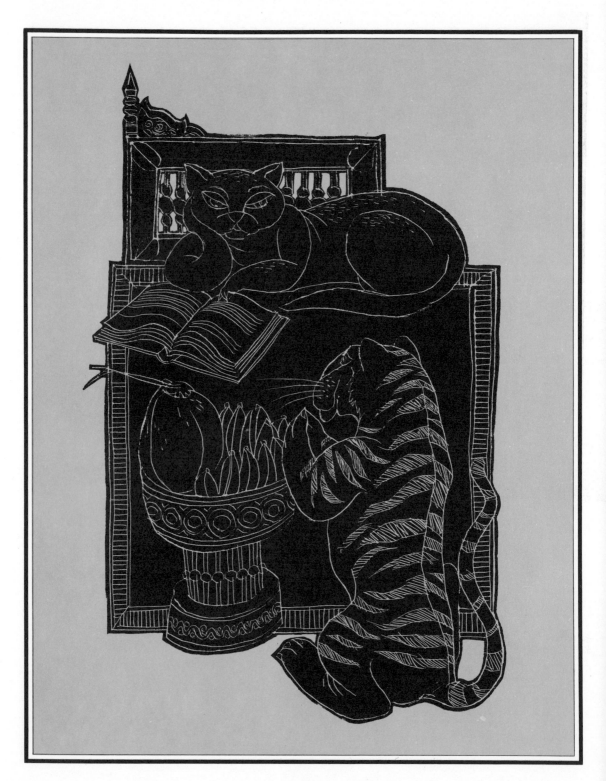

for he is stronger and bigger than I am." So he decided that he would not teach the tiger one special trick.

The three years of apprenticeship drew to an end, and the tiger respectfully asked, "Sire Teacher, have I learned everything?"

"Everything," replied the cat untruthfully. The tiger thanked the cat and went away joyfully.

The tiger now started hunting on his own, but he was soon disappointed with himself, for as he crouched to spring on a doe, the latter seemed to know that she was in danger and ran away. He again crouched to spring on a bullock, and again the tiger failed to get his prey. "Hide yourself well and surprise your prey" was one of the maxims of his teacher, the cat, and he had hidden himself well behind a bamboo thicket, but both the doe and the bullock knew that he was there. He was puzzled and, crouching as if to spring, he considered his position carefully. At last he realized that the thud, thud of his tail, as he moved it, served as a warning to his would-be victims. "It is that treacherous cat!" he cried out in anger. "He never taught me to move my tail about without making a noise."

His anger increased when he remembered how quiet was the cat's tail when on a hunt. And he swore that he would go out, find the cat and eat him up.

So it is, from that day on, the tiger keeps looking for the cat but hasn't found him. For there is another trick that the cat did not teach his pupil. Wherever he happens to be, the cat always covers his dung with earth or ashes, thus making his trail more difficult to follow.

THE GOLDEN CROW

LONG AGO THERE LIVED an old widow who was very poor. She had a daughter who was pretty and good-natured.

One day the mother asked the daughter to scare away the birds from the tray of paddy which was being dried in the sun. So the daughter sat down near the tray and scared away the birds. When the paddy was nearly dried, however, a strange bird came flying towards the tray. It was a crow with gold feathers. The Golden Crow laughed at the little girl's efforts to scare him away and quickly ate up every bit of the rice, chaff and all.

The girl started to cry, saying, "Oh, my mother is so poor! My mother is so poor! The rice is so valuable to her."

The Golden Crow gave her a kindly look and said, "Little girl, I will pay for it. Come to the big tamarind tree outside the village at sunset, and I will give you something." Then the crow flew away.

At sunset, the little girl went to the big tamarind tree and looked up at the branches. To her surprise, she saw a little house of gold at the top.

The crow looked out of a window of the little golden house, and said, "Oh, there you are! Do come up. But, of course, I must drop the ladder first. Do you want the golden ladder, the silver ladder, or the brass ladder?"

"I am only a poor little girl," replied the girl, "and I can only ask for the brass ladder." To her surprise, the crow put down the golden ladder, and the little girl climbed up on it to the little gold house.

"You must have dinner with me," invited the crow. "But let me see, do you want the gold dish, the silver dish, or the brass dish to eat your food from?"

"I am only a poor little girl," she replied, "and I can only ask for the brass dish." To her surprise, the crow brought out the gold dish, and the food in it was delicious.

"You are a good little girl," said the crow, when the little girl had finished eating, "and I would like you to stay here with me forever. But your mother needs you more, so I must send you back before it gets too dark."

Then he went into the bedroom, and brought out a big box, a medium-sized box, and a small box. "Choose one of these boxes," said the crow, "and give it to your mother."

"The paddy you ate was not much," replied the girl, "and the little box would be more than enough." She then accepted the little box and, after thanking the Golden Crow, climbed down the golden ladder and went home.

When she reached there, she gave the little box to her mother. Together they opened it, and they were surprised and delighted to find in the box a hundred priceless rubies. The mother and daughter became very rich and lived in luxury.

There was another old widow in the village, but she was not poor. She also had a daughter, who, however, was greedy and bad tempered. This widow and her daughter heard about the gift of the Golden Crow, and became very jealous of the other widow and her daughter.

They decided to try to get a similar gift for themselves. So they put out a tray of paddy in the sun, and the greedy girl kept watch. But as she was lazy, she did not try to scare away the birds that came to eat up the paddy. When the Golden Crow at last turned up, there were very few grains left.

However, the Golden Crow ate what remained, and the greedy girl shouted rudely, "Hey, crow, give me and my mother some wealth for the paddy you have eaten."

The crow looked at her with a frown, but he replied politely enough, "Little girl, I will pay for the rice. Come to the big tamarind tree outside the village at sunset, and I will give you something." Then the crow flew away.

At sunset, the greedy girl went to the big tamarind tree, and without waiting for the crow to come out, she shouted, "Hey, crow, keep your promise."

The crow put his head out of the window and asked, "On which ladder do you want to climb up here? The golden ladder, the silver ladder or the brass ladder?"

"The golden ladder, of course," replied the greedy girl. But, to her disappointment, the crow lowered the brass ladder.

When the girl entered the little gold house, the crow said, "You must dine with me. Do you want to eat your food from the gold dish, the silver dish or the brass dish?"

"The gold dish, of course," replied the greedy girl. But to her disappointment, it was the brass dish she was served.

The food was delicious but it was no more than a tiny morsel, and the greedy girl was annoyed. Then the crow went into the bedroom and brought out a big box, a medium-sized box, and a small box, and said, "Choose one of these boxes and give it to your mother."

The greedy girl, of course, chose the big box, and without re-membering to thank the crow, she struggled down the ladder with her burden.

When she reached home, she and her mother joyfully pulled open the big box. But to their surprise and terror, a big snake lay coiled inside. The snake hissed at them angrily, and then glided out of the box and out of their house.

THE CASE OF THE CALF AND THE COLT

MISTER CLEVER and Mister Stupid were neighbors. Mister Clever had a cow, whereas Mister Stupid had a mare.

One night Clever's cow gave birth to a calf, and Stupid's mare gave birth to a colt. Clever, being a light sleeper, heard the bleating of the calf and the neighing of the colt. Taking a light, he went down to the cowshed to have a look. He noticed that there was no light in Stupid's stable. Guessing that Stupid had not been awakened by the neighing of the colt, Clever took the calf to the stable, and brought the colt to the cowshed. Then he went back to bed.

Early the next day he went round the village, telling everybody that a strange and wonderful thing had happened; his cow had given birth to a colt. The villagers flocked to the cowshed and gazed in wonder at the colt. By this time, Stupid had found the calf in his stable and, suspecting the truth, he came to Clever and accused him of stealing his colt. Clever denied it, maintaining that by a strange freak of nature, his cow had given birth to a colt. "But what about the calf in my stable?" Stupid asked indignantly.

"By a strange freak of nature, also," suggested Clever sweetly, "your mare must have given birth to a calf."

Stupid appealed to the neighbors who, however, admitted their inability to decide the dispute. So Stupid asked Clever to go with him to another village to find a judge. On the way they met a rabbit and asked him to act as judge in their dispute.

"With pleasure," replied the rabbit.

Stupid and Clever explained what the dispute was, and the rabbit said, "I am busy now, but will fix a date for your case. I will meet

you in your village at sunrise on the morning of the seventh day from now. Be ready with your witnesses." Stupid and Clever thanked the rabbit, and went back to their village.

On the appointed day at sunrise Stupid and Clever and the whole village assembled to await the coming of Judge Rabbit. The sun rose higher and higher until it was noon, but there was no Judge Rabbit. Noon passed and still there was no Judge Rabbit. It was only at sunset that the rabbit appeared. As it was so unusual for the rabbit to break his word, the villagers could not help asking why he did not come at the appointed time, although in ordinary circumstances they should, out of courtesy, have asked no questions of a judge.

"I am so sorry," replied Judge Rabbit, " but I was delayed by an accident. As I was coming to you this morning, I saw a sandbank

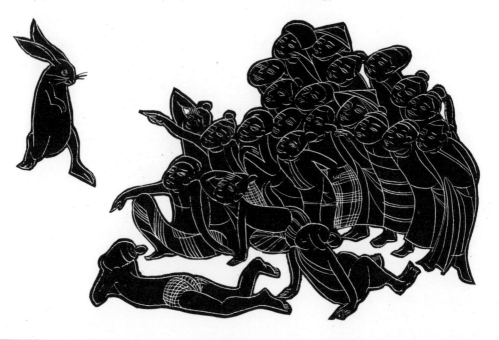

in the river on fire, and the whole day I have been carrying water in a wicker crate and pouring it on the fire to put it out."

Clever, who took pride in his cleverness, thought that Judge Rabbit was trying to test the intelligence of the villagers. "Sire Judge," said he brightly, "how can a sandbank in the middle of the river be on fire, and how can water be carried in a wicker crate? It is against nature. I do not believe you!"

"Quite right, Mister Clever," replied Judge Rabbit calmly. "How can a cow give birth to a colt, and how can a mare give birth to a calf? It is against nature. So take back your calf and give back the colt to your neighbor Mister Stupid."

The villagers applauded the decision of Judge Rabbit, and from that day onwards they always chose the rabbit as their judge in all their disputes.

THE BEE-HUNTER AND THE OOZIE

THE BEE-HUNTER SAW a large hive on a tree and, climbing it, he smoked out the bees from the hive. As the bees were very angry and persistent, he was quite tired and dizzy by the time they finally fled and the hive was ready for him to take. When he stretched out his hands to seize hold of the hive, he lost his balance and fell. But fortunately he was able to catch hold of a tree branch with his left hand. He remained there dangling, unable to pull himself up with one hand, and frightened to let go of the branch since he was still some distance away from the ground.

He shouted for help, and an *oozie* astride his elephant came in answer to his shouts. The *oozie*, sitting on his elephant, stopped right under the bee-hunter. He lifted up his driving spear, saying, "My friend, do not be afraid, but just slide down my driving spear onto my shoulders and then onto the back of my elephant."

The bee-hunter, in great joy, caught hold of the point of the driving spear with his right hand, but at that very moment the huge beast moved away, so that the *oozie* was also left dangling in the air, clutching onto his driving spear.

"Now, be careful," exclaimed the *oozie*, "do not let go of the branch and do not let go of my driving spear. Be patient and be strong. Help will come soon."

Some minutes passed, and the bee-hunter said, "My friend, my hands are getting tired and I must save myself by letting go."

"Don't do it!" protested the *oozie*. "I am in this plight only because I tried to save you."

As the two went on arguing, four young men came along. When they saw the predicament of the bee-hunter and the *oozie*, one of the young men took off his *longyi* and he and his three companions held it stretched out underneath the *oozie* and the bee-hunter. Then they shouted, "Jump! Jump!"

The *oozie* and the bee-hunter jumped and landed on the outspread *longyi*. But the force of their weight caused the young men to fall forward, knocking their four heads together.

All had to be treated by a physician, and the question of paying the fee, which amounted to six silver coins, arose. The young men

maintained that the other two should pay, because they were hurt in saving the bee-hunter and the *oozie's* lives.

The *oozie* maintained that the physician's fee should be paid by the bee-hunter, as the *oozie* got into trouble in trying to rescue the bee-hunter.

The bee-hunter argued that, although he did not want to be ungrateful, he was not under any obligation to pay the fee, as the young men and the *oozie* freely undertook to save his life on humanitarian grounds.

The dispute finally reached the Princess Learned-in-the-Law and her judgment was as follows:

"Just because the four young men, of their own accord and on humanitarian grounds, freely offered their assistance to the two dangling men, it did not mean that they had surrendered their legal right to compensation for any injury or loss. On the other hand, in effecting the rescue, they were under an obligation to use due care and caution. The same legal principles apply to the *oozie*.

"Therefore, we must consider who were responsible for the injury caused to all six, and we find that none of the six was quite free from blame. It was negligent of the *oozie* to lift up his spear to the bee-hunter, without first ensuring that his elephant would not move away. The bee-hunter was also careless in not anticipating the likelihood of the elephant moving forward. The four young men were also negligent in not anticipating that the weight of the two dangling men falling on the cloth *longyi* would throw them off their balance.

"But the degree of negligence was not the same. The bee-hunter was the root of the dispute, and so he shall contribute one silver coin towards the physician's fee. The *oozie* was the trunk of the dispute, and so he shall contribute three silver coins. The four young men were the branch of the dispute, and so they shall contribute together two silver coins."

THE OLD MAN IN THE MOON

ONCE THERE WAS an old man in a village, and he earned his living by pounding paddy. He had no friend or companion except an old rabbit. The whole day, and part of the night when there was a moon, the old man pounded the paddy, and the old rabbit crouched nearby, eating the chaff that his master threw away.

One moonlit night the old man, while pounding the paddy, said to himself, "It is sheer waste of time sifting the grain from the chaff after pounding. If only I had an old woman with me, she could do the sifting, and also keep me and my rabbit company."

The Moon-goddess heard his words and felt sorry for him. The next day, taking the form of an old woman, she came to the old man and kept him company. The whole day she sifted with a sieve the grain from the chaff, while the old man pounded the paddy. At nightfall, she went back to the sky.

Every day the Moon-goddess changed herself into an old woman and kept the old man and the rabbit company. At nightfall she always went away, for if it was a moonlit night she had to go and look after her moon, and if it was a moonless night the old man did not need her help as he did not work in the dark.

Weeks went by in this manner, until the old man asked, "Who are you? Why do you go away when night falls?"

The old woman replied that she was the Moon-goddess.

"Take me and my rabbit to your moon," pleaded the old man, "and let us live with you forever, for we are so lonely without you." So the Moon-goddess took the old man and the rabbit to her moon and let them stay with her forever.

When the moon is full, you can see the old man still pounding rice up there, and the rabbit still eating the chaff that the old man throws away.

THE DRUNKARD AND THE OPIUM-EATER

ONCE IN A VILLAGE there lived a drunkard and an opium-eater. Both outcasts of society, they became fast friends. Having no house of their own, they spent their time in the various rest houses of the village. But they avoided one particular rest house, namely the one at the cemetery, for all believed that it was the nightly meeting-place of the village ghosts.

One evening, however, the drunkard was more intoxicated than usual and, in spite of the entreaties and warnings of his friend, the opium-eater, he went to spend the night at the cemetery rest house, taking with him many pots of toddy. He reached the rest house and sat drinking. As he became more and more intoxicated he became bolder and his mind more alert. He did not feel sleepy at all.

About midnight two or three ghosts came in, but before they could suspect that he was a human being, the drunkard calmly said, "Hello fellows. You are late today, or am I early?"

Other ghosts came in until the rest house was absolutely full. One of the ghosts looked around and said, "I smell human flesh. I suspect the presence of a stranger."

"Why not count us," suggested another ghost.

The drunkard at once stood up and shouted, "One, two, three, four. One, two, three, four. All correct, all correct."

The ghosts believed him and settled down to talk about various matters. "Do you know, gentlemen," one talkative ghost said, "that underneath where I am sitting there lie buried seven pots of gold?"

The drunkard carefully noted where the speaker was sitting.

The talk went on until dawn, when the ghosts went away. The drunkard dug up the seven pots of gold and became very rich. He bought a house and lived in luxury with his friend, the opium-eater.

The opium-eater, however, was not satisfied. He wanted to have seven pots of gold, also. So he prevailed upon his friend, the drunkard, to tell him the secret of how he found the pots of gold. After the opium-eater had listened to his friend's story, he decided to spend the night at the cemetery rest house.

He duly went there but, as he was full of opium, he became very sleepy. When the ghosts came into the rest house at midnight he was half-asleep. The ghosts looked at him with suspicion. Other ghosts came in, until the rest house was absolutely full.

One ghost said that he could smell human flesh, and suspected the presence of a human being among them. Another ghost reminded the company that some nights before a human being had been present and had run off with seven pots of gold after listening to their talk. A third ghost stood up and started to count the company. All the time the opium-eater was too sleepy to do anything to prevent his presence from being discovered. The ghost finished counting and reported that there was one extra.

Those ghosts who had suspected the opium-eater from the beginning, seized and carefully scrutinized him. When they saw that he was a human being, they pulled his nose until it became fully three yards long. Then all the ghosts silently departed.

The next morning the drunkard went to look for his friend at the rest house and found him half dead with fear. The drunkard helped the opium-eater to his feet, and took him home. As the two friends walked through the streets, all the villagers roared with laughter to see the three-yard-long nose of the opium-eater.

"Friend," consoled the drunkard, "I will go tonight and find out the cure for your long nose."

When night came the drunkard went to the cemetery rest house after fortifying himself with many pots of toddy. He waited until two or three ghosts came in. Then he said cheerfully, "Hello, you fellows, I came early hoping to find a human being in the rest house again. Last night I had no fun at all, for you people crowded round him and gave me no chance to get at his nose."

The ghosts had all assembled, and one ghost suggested that the company be carefully counted because he could smell human flesh. The drunkard, alert as ever, stood up and shouted, "One, two, three, four! One, two, three, four! All correct, all correct."

The ghosts believed him, and started to talk. "By the way," said the drunkard during a lull in the conversation, "we did have great fun last night with that fellow's nose. Out of sheer curiosity, I want to know whether it will ever be the right length again."

"Yes," answered a wise-looking ghost, "provided, of course, that the right remedy is applied. If the fellow touches the tip of his nose

with a pestle, the nose will shrink half an inch, and if he does that repeatedly it will become the right length again.'' The drunkard changed the conversation. When the ghosts had gone away with the coming of dawn, the drunkard returned to his friend, the opium-eater, and told him the glad news. The opium-eater used the pestle with due care and deliberation, so that his nose should not become too short. And at last it became the right size again.

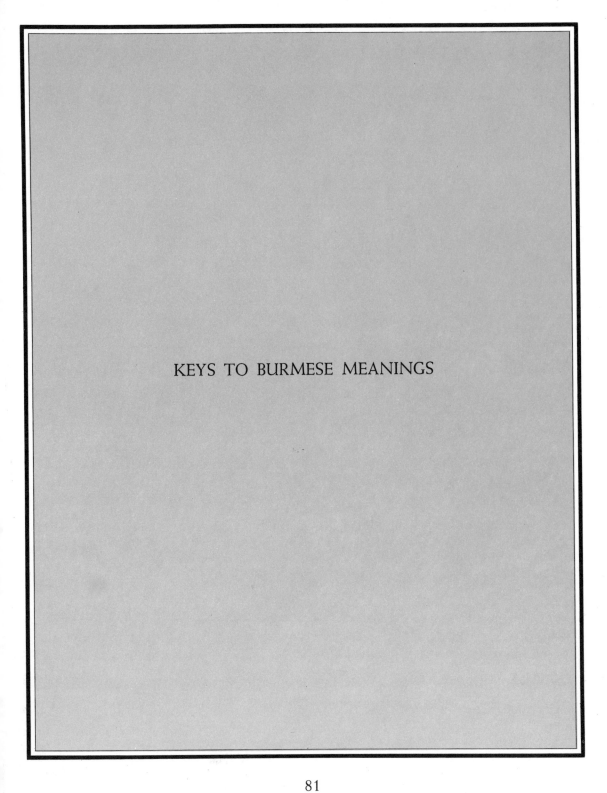

KEYS TO BURMESE MEANINGS

BAMBOO: In Burma, hardly anything is as useful as bamboo. Rub two bamboo sticks together and you make a fire. Blow on the fire with a bamboo bellows and the fire glows brightly. When the paddy birds swoop down to eat the rice seedlings, frighten them away with a noisy bamboo clapper. Rest on a cool bamboo mat in your house, with rafters, walls and floors of bamboo (see p. 33 and 56); furnish your house with objects and utensils of bamboo.

Celebrate the harvest with family and friends. Sing and dance to music made on bamboo instruments. Enjoy the cooking aroma of *kaukhnyin*, the glutenous rice with salt, roasted in a section of bamboo. When it is done, eat it as you sit near the wood fire in the cool of the early morning.

Burma bamboo grows tall, as tall as a hundred feet. It grows fast. Some say that in 24 hours it has been known to grow 18 inches.

BASKETS: Everyone uses baskets, and there is a right one for every use. And the right time to make them is between harvest and the first rain. Nature supplies the materials—bamboo, reed and rattan; the whole family supplies the skill and the labor.

If you are bringing piglets, peacocks, strawberries or sunflower seeds to market, put them in baskets. Choose huge floppy ones for barnyard fowls or animals. For small-grained or powdery things like dried beans, groundnuts, sesamum, cinnamon or seminola, the deep, square-bottomed, rigid-sided baskets with wide mouths are more suitable (see p. 56). They fit nicely on the head. So, too, do the baskets of the road repair and construction workers. These are shallow, firmly woven, bowl-shaped baskets for sand, stones and mud. A twist of cloth under a basket helps to keep it from slipping.

Fish are caught in baskets. Rice is measured by baskets. Housewives market with a basket on the arm. Mothers fold away clothing in baskets. The prettiest basket in the house, and the one that gets the most attention, is the cradle. Whether indoors or out, everyone gives it a push to help swing baby to sleep.

BEES AND BEE HUNTING: Bees are not raised, kept or otherwise domesticated in Burma. A man who wants honey or beeswax must go hunting for it. Success depends upon a combination of skills. A bee-hunter should be a powerful cigar smoker, an agile tree climber and a good holder-on-er. His problems are complicated by the fact that not all bees build the same kind of nests. The common tree bee constructs a hive that hangs from a tree branch. The dammer bee, on the other hand, nests in a tree trunk cavity. To puff vigorously on a cigar while hugging the trunk of a tree, or while balancing on a branch, can be harder on the bee-hunter than on the bees (see p. 66).

If the honey doesn't seem worth the effort, the wax must be. It is said that in Burma, the dammer bee produces a wax so tough, it is used to calk the seams of boats.

DAH: A *dah* is not the bleat of an animal; it is the word in Burmese that means a blade.

A villager, even a good Buddhist and therefore prohibited from taking life, normally tucks a *dah* at his waist before stepping out of his house —not because he is nervous or has evil intentions, but because he is practical. Who knows? Perhaps the wheels of his cart will need fixing, a neighbor will need a hand with finishing his house, or he'll pass some firewood on the way.

Blades for different uses have specific names. Usually *dah* is part of the name. A *dahmah*, "main blade," is the mainstay of every kitchen. It is the kitchen chopping knife that doubles for cleaving the kindling, or chores that call for an axe. A *dahhmyoung*, "clinging blade," is a dagger. A *dahlwe*, "blade strung across the shoulder," a slender sword in a bamboo or cane handle, is the weapon of soldiers (see p. 44). A *Shandah* is the handsomest *dah* of them all. As the name suggests, this *dah* is made by *Shan* swordsmiths. It is always ornate, massive in proportions and sheathed in a silver scabbard.

FOOTWEAR: The best way to stay cool, and the next best thing to going barefoot is to wear *pha nats*, Burmese sandals (see p. 75). They consist of leather or rubber soles, and thongs to hold them on, usually of velvet or soft leather. *Pha nat* means "to be trodden on."

Men, women and children wear *pha nats*, although children run barefooted whenever and as long as they can. During the rainy season, to keep out of the mud, people prefer wooden clogs. But whatever the season or the shoe, it is the custom to remove footwear before entering a house, a pagoda, or certain other specified areas like the *pongyi kyaung,* where the Buddhist monks study and live.

GONGS AND GONGSMAN: In the olden days, when Burma was ruled by kings, official announcements were broadcast throughout the royal cities by servants of the king. The group that went forth with news always included one who was a gongsman (see p. 35). As the gong that he carried had to produce a deep, strong sound, it had to be large and heavy. So it was suspended on a stout pole and supported by at least two men. But the gongsman was the one who sounded the gong. He did so with a striker of wood, padded at the end with wool felt or leather to mellow the sound.

Though gongsmen are gone, gongs are still made and used in modern Burma. In the cities, a well-off family employs servants, and among them there is a watchman. He makes his rounds and strikes a gong on the hour to indicate that all is well, and also, that he isn't off somewhere or asleep.

A Burmese orchestra wouldn't be complete without a gong musician. He sits right in the middle of his circle of graduated sizes of gongs, like a king on a throne. The stand on which the gongs rest is always exquisitely carved of wood, decorated in bright red lacquer, studded with tiny bits of mirrors, and gilded so that it catches the light.

At every pagoda there's a gong. It is large, made of bronze, hung on a teak stand built to support its great weight. Close to it there is a padded striker. On leaving the pagoda, adults and children, too, strike the big gong and the sound echoes in the air. In this way, all within hearing share in the merit that the persons acquired by going to the pagoda.

GUDGEON: A freshwater fish common to Burma, considered a member of the carp family. It is a tasty fish fried until it becomes golden brown and very crisp (see the story, "Partnership").

HAIR STYLES: Both Burmese men and women used to wear long hair. A few men in the villages still do and they wear it in the old-fashioned way—pulled tight into a knot at the top or to the side of the head (see p. 19 and 30). Women still wear their hair long and the style hasn't changed very much. They tie their hair at the back of the head, sometimes with a strand flowing (see p. 56), or fasten it like a crown, adding hair not their own. A little garland of jasmine, or a freshly picked blossom is an everyday touch. On special occasions the ladies like to wear jeweled hair ornaments as well.

The hair style of witches in Burma hasn't changed much either (see p. 42). They still wear it hanging down as witches do elsewhere.

Burmese children, especially in the villages, wear a hairstyle today that has been the same for a long, long time. Both boys and girls wear a short-long combination. There is a short fringe of hair, about two inches, cut like bangs completely around the head. The hair at the crown of the head grows long, and this is pulled up into a topknot. Young children have their "long" hair tied with a ribbon into a ponytail that points up (see p. 72). The back of the head is shaved all the way up to meet the fringe which gives Burmese children a charming long-necked look.

HEADGEAR: Burmese women usually go bareheaded, except, of course, for a flower. If there is a hot sun and work requires being exposed to it, a woman puts on something, but merely for protection—anything at all to fend off heat prostration—a piece of cloth tied on casually, an old straw hat, but the headgear doesn't matter. Not so the men.

Young or old, a Burmese man chooses his hat with deliberation. A most common "head wrap," the *gaungbaung*, is a kind of turban. It might be one in colored silk to match his *longyi*, or, more commonly, in white cotton muslin, neatly tied with ends pointing up, just so (see p. 37). Sometimes a man likes a wide-brimmed hat of bark (see p. 14) or cane, and in the present day, a cool pith helmet, a snug knitted stocking cap, or balaclava, and then there's always the felt fedora. The deciding factor might be mood, weather, the work to be done, the occasion. In a particular region of the country, there is often a typical headgear for men. They say it is possible to tell where a man is from by the manner in which he ties the "head wrap," or by the hat he is wearing.

HOUSE LIZARD: The house lizard (see p. 29), a species of gecko, and commonly called that in Burma, is not as the name implies, a pet or domesticated creature like the house cat. But a gecko isn't anyone's enemy either, except of course of the smaller creatures that it feeds upon. At full growth it is a couple of inches long; almost from birth it is acrobatic. The house lizard comes into a house and just stays on. It multiplies rapidly. Fascinating to watch, there is almost no place that it cannot get to with its suction padded feet. The house lizard walks upside down on ceilings to pursue its prey, mostly flies and mosquitoes. One flick of the tongue and there's no need for a flyswatter.

KING'S CHAMBERLAIN: The kings of Burma, as kings everywhere, lived amid luxury in great palaces. They had many attendants, officers, ministers and a great many servants. In the royal household, the individual who had the responsibility for management or supervision of the king's living quarters, as distinct from the rest of the royal establishment and the Court, was the king's chamberlain (see "The Fisherman and the King's Chamberlain").

LONGYI: A *longyi* is the name of the garment that Burmese adults and children of both sexes wear. It is a skirt from waist to ankles that is tied on. There are no hooks, buttons or zippers. The boys and men tie it on at front, center, with a deep pleat, shake out the folds, tug it, then twist and tie the ends. The girls and the ladies pull the cloth to one side, also make a deep pleat, tug it, twist it, but tuck in the ends. The garment is worn very gracefully (see p. 22).

For work or just around the house, you'd wear a cotton *longyi*. For going out, a silk one. Both would be handwoven, although machine-made fabrics are also popular today. It is a practical, comfortable garment for a tropical country like Burma. It is cool and adaptable. When caught in the rain, or a sudden chilling breeze, pull your *longyi* up over your shoulders, or wear it like a hood. To make boys' "shorts," when there's a tree to be climbed or active work to be done (see p. 19), gather it up and pull it through your legs; tuck it into the back waistband.

If there is a grand event such as a wedding, gentlemen wear the super *longyi* called a *pasoe*. It is about six yards long, of splendid rustling silk cloth. In the Burmese Court, it was the custom for courtiers, ministers and of course the king, to wear this luxurious type of *longyi* (see p. 37).

MATS: Burmese mats, called *hpyas*, are important to every household and always have been. Rolled up when not in use, taken along on family journeys, plain or fancy, mats are always cool, light and flexible. (see p. 37).

There are mats for sleeping, eating, for visitors, for kneeling at the family altar, and the pagoda. A teacher and a student might sit together or separately on mats (see p. 54).

The finest kind are woven of grasses called *thin*. But reed fibers, *thabaw*, make fine mats also. Some are woven in geometric patterns, others have designs in color. There are bound and unbound mats, square and rectangular mats. Those for sleeping have a shape to indicate head and foot ends.

MONSOON: This word, monsoon, is not Burmese. It's Arabic. It was, and still is, used to name the winds that blow from the Southwest in summer and the Northeast in winter. In Burma's "summer," or rainy season, these winds bring rain from May until October. The rainy season has come to be called the "monsoon." It is the period when the fields that have been parched dry to dust are renewed again by the drenching rain, when the paddy and other crops have their time to grow.

During the monsoon season, it may rain continuously for several days, but on some days it rains fitfully. Some regions have as much as 220 inches of rain a season, as on the Arakan Coast, while the central dry zone may have as little as 30 inches. As in the story, "Mister Luck and Mister Industry," it sometimes is raining in one place and is dry in another.

MORTAR: To pound, crush or pulverize in a vessel called a mortar with an implement called a pestle is not a Burmese invention. But Burma is a place where the use of mortars has been continuous and long. The word for mortar in Burmese is *sone*.

In a Burmese kitchen, a mortar is used in the preparation of food. Ingredients for curries would not be properly blended if the cook didn't use a mortar. The favorite spice in a Burmese meal is chili, hot red peppers. So much chili is crushed in the mortar, and so frequently, the kitchen mortar is referred to as "the chili mortar," *ngayoke-sone*.

Grains are pounded in huge mortars (see p. 72). The pestle is so big that two people may take turns, alternating every other toss of the pounder.

NAGA: The *Naga* is one of five Burmese mythical creatures and undoubtedly the best known. Some almost believe that the *Naga* is real. It is a huge dragon, the favorite motif of Burmese artists, whether they are painting, working in silver, or carving wood.

The *Naga* (see p. 25) lives underground and on the floor of the sea. It is quite capable of causing earthquakes and whirlpools. At will, the *Naga* can turn itself into the form of a human being. However, if it should fall asleep, back it turns into a *Naga* again, automatically. Ordinarily, a *Naga* has little to do with people. Its sphere is the animal kingdom. It has one enemy, the *Galon*, an enormous bird, also mythical. But except for that enemy, the *Naga* is all-powerful.

OGRE: So long as anyone can remember, a Burmese demon, or ogre, has always looked as he does on page 49. Since the ogre, sometimes called a *bilu*, wears the same fierce expression, has the same dress, never appears to be younger or to get older, he's recognized anywhere for what he is, an ogre. Supposedly, ogres devour human beings. But there are those who claim that they only eat bad people. Whichever is the truth, this character of Burmese legend, dance and theatre, though fearsome, is popular in a curious sort of way. Few would want to meet up with an ogre, but most rather like to talk about what a monster the ogre is. It's a way that grownups use to get little children to stop being naughty.

OOZIE: An elephant driver is called *oozie* in Burmese. This is a kind of abbreviation for *hsin oozie*, the full name (*hsin*, elephant; *oozie*, leader, guide). But an *oozie*, in English or in Burmese, represents much more than that. He not only is the leader, guide, driver, he is the elephant's trainer, his nurse, his friend and guardian. An *oozie* knows his elephant better than anyone else in the world. And why shouldn't he? An *oozie* and an elephant grow up together. A boy as young as five, with an elephant of the same age, might begin to be an *oozie*. That means that the boy and the animal play together and come to trust each other. Soon the boy will teach the elephant what is expected of him. This will include the most important training of the elephant as a work animal.

In the great teakwood forests of Burma, elephants are used for a large part of the work of lifting and transporting timber. The lumber mills also employ elephants as labor. With each working elephant, there's an *oozie* who has devoted his life to his animal. Since elephants and men have about the same life span, some *oozies* and their charges live together for fifty or sixty years.

PADDY: Paddy is the name of the plant that produces the pearl white grain called rice. The man who plants the rice fields is called a paddy farmer, and the fields are called paddy fields. The white, long-legged slender birds that try to eat the young seedlings in the paddy fields are called paddy birds. The large teakwood boats that transport paddy to the mills are called paddy boats (see p. 19). The mills are known as rice mills, for they handle the rice grain.

PAGODA: Whether one calls Buddhism a religion or a Way of Life, the pagoda is the place where Buddhists come to worship and to pray. The pagoda building may be constructed in any one of several forms. Some have large indoor spaces, like churches, synagogues and mosques, or are solid, like a pyramid. The most usual Burmese pagoda shape is like a bell. There are many pagodas in Burma, and of all sizes (see p. 67). The domes of some are covered with gold leaf and gleam in the sunlight. Many are white.

A man who builds or gilds a pagoda, big or small, gains merit in this and the next world. The Burmese word *hpaya* is used both for a pagoda and for the image of the Buddha.

PARASOL: For many, many years, a parasol has been the fashionable sun-shade of Burmese ladies. Some wouldn't go out without one. A parasol lends a festive air to even an ordinary day. Made of a bamboo frame, shaft and ribs, it is lightweight to carry. The cover of cotton or rayon, in ice-cream colors, is always decorated with handpainted flowers in a contrasting color. The tip end, painted black, has a little silver ring through which a strand of wool is looped with two pompoms. The pompoms bob up and down with the motion of the parasol, opened or closed. The handle is usually covered with a bit of hammered silver, Burmese style.

In a parasol-making family, children learn to make or assemble parts of the parasol. Children are especially adept at pompoms, tying and snipping ends or tipping paint on the end of each rib. The work on parasols is done outdoors, in front of the house or in the shade under it. Anyone can watch, even join in. (See p. 14 for a large, practical parasol.)

PONGYI: A man who takes Buddhist vows and enters the religious order called the *Sangha*, is a *pongyi* (see p. 35). A *pongyi*, sometimes referred to as a monk, gives up material possessions, has his head shaven, dons the simple yellow robes of the Order, and lives a quiet life inside the walls of the *pongyi kyaung*. There he is guided by strict rules for behavior and the routines around which his life is regulated. A *pongyi*, for example, may not touch money, or eat anything after the noon hour. Every morning at the sound of the gong, *pongyis* go forth, each with a big bowl, to collect a donation of rice (see p. 35) from every Buddhist household in the village. The family that gives gains merit for so doing. A *pongyi* spends many hours studying and is frequently a teacher of Buddhist scripture.

PRINCESS LEARNED-IN-THE-LAW: The Princess might have been real, but she wasn't. Though only a folktale character, she represents the Burmese view that women have ability. In the past, and today, Burmese women have wielded power in business, and have had responsible positions in the professions and in government. In a village, for example, the wisest, most trusted individual is chosen by common consent as the headman, or *thugyi*. Men more often than women are chosen. But women have been *thugyi*, and in that role they listen to and settle disputes.

In Burma today, women are elected to sit in the Parliament, they have been sent to participate in the United Nations and to serve as ambassadors abroad. Like the Princess Learned-in-the-Law, they, too, try to settle disputes and wisely reestablish harmony.

REST HOUSE: Most every village has a rest house, *zayat*, and a town may have several. It is a simple structure that offers any passer-by or weary traveler a place to stop for rest and for shelter. Usually, it is a wooden platform with a roof (see p. 76).

An individual or a group builds a *zayat* as a donation to others. It is an act of merit.

There are family as well as public rest houses, on pagoda grounds or on the grounds of other religious buildings. Buddhists use a rest house for quiet contemplation, fasting, and sometimes to spend the night. Visitors to the *kyaung*, where Buddhist monks study and live, use the rest house provided for their comfort. Some *zayats* in the shade of venerable trees are merely raised platforms without a roof. Cemeteries often have rest houses for tired mourners.

RICE CAKE: The big rice cake Master Thumb asked his mother to make in the story, "How Master Thumb Defeated the Sun," is a pancake of rice flour sweetened with jaggery, the sugar made from sap of the palm tree. In Burmese this flapjack is called *mont pyit salet*. And it is pronounced just as it is spelled.

Rice cakes and all kinds of pastries, as well as confections, are snacks enjoyed anytime in the day, rather than as dessert. Fresh fruits are eaten at the end of a meal.

SERVING AND SITTING: A Burmese family of ordinary circumstances puts down a mat where the meal will be served; the food is brought in a large round receptacle on its own pedestal. The family gathers around the *htaminok*, "rice container," which is usually made of lacquered wood. Although called a rice container, this receptacle is used for serving fruit and other foods also (see p. 54).

Sitting on chairs is a foreign notion. Indeed, the Burmese word for a chair is *kalahtine*, or "that on which a foreigner sits." Burmese people sit on their haunches with complete ease (see p. 14). There's no problem about having enough chairs, except for foreigners, of course.

SESAMUM: The oil from crushed *sesamum* seeds is excellent for cooking. Roasted, the tiny seeds have a nutlike flavor and are used for garnishing salads, cooked food and baked goods. *Sesamum* candy bars are delicious.

Around Mandalay, in the dry zone, the farmers plant *sesamum* as an alternate crop to cotton. The story, "Why the Rabbit's Nose Twitches," and many others in this collection, originally came from that region of Burma. In the *Arabian Nights* tales, the magic words were "Open, Sesame," but not in Burma. In Burma, it is *sesamum* or *sesamin*.

TAMARIND TREE: A popular shade tree, the tamarind is planted for its beauty as well as for its utility. It grows to about the size of an oak and it is as sturdy. The fruit has medicinal value and is enjoyed both green and ripe. Children save the shiny black fruit pits for a kind of flicking-to-hit-down game. The feathery green leaf of the tamarind has a flavor that comes out nicely in broth. Tamarind improves good curries with a touch of sharp sourness that blends with the chilies. *Magyi* is the Burmese name for tamarind tree (see p. 56).

TATTOOS AND TATTOOING: In olden days, tattoos were believed to give one magical powers. Men had themselves tattooed to charm away evil. It was the Burmese custom to be tattooed from the waist down (see p. 37).

The process of tattooing designs into the skin was not only painful but it frequently caused infections. Yet men were regarded as manlier for being tattooed and women would have nothing to do with a man who wasn't. There were standard designs with special meanings, depending upon the superstitions that were current at the time.

The practice of tattooing is no longer popular and has all but disappeared.

TODDY: Toddy is an alcoholic beverage. Several types of palm tree in Burma produce the liquid which when fermented becomes toddy. Boiled fresh, the unfermented juice makes a sugar called jaggery, that resembles maple sugar and tastes like it. But, whereas the sap from the maple tree is tapped from a slash in the trunk, palm sap is from the stalk of the flower of the tree. The palmyra is the palm used most by the Burmese toddy gatherer. He's known as a toddy-climber (see p. 31). The juice of one palm amounts to about a gallon in 24 hours.

VILLAGER'S HOUSE: Most of the families of Burma live in villages. The houses they live in all look alike; they have been constructed of the same materials and in the same way for a long, long time (see p. 35).

Nature provides the villager with most of the materials he needs to build his house—except for the *dah* and the hammer and nails. His family and neighbors together, supply the labor. When completed, the villager's house is a modest dwelling, as the home of every proper Burmese Buddhist family should be.

WATER JARS: The containers in which water is either fetched or stored are called water jars. In Burma, these are usually of earthenware, which stays cool. Sometimes the jars are glazed halfway down for added strength. The shape is quite distinctive (see p. 79 and 22).

The long dry season makes water a precious thing. Yet, Burmese people share water with strangers. Anyone who travels in Burma knows that even in a remote village you need not go thirsty, for there is always an outdoor *ye oh sin,* or water-jar rack, with a dipper alongside. Sometimes the rack will have a little roof to keep off the heat of the sun's rays. There is a Burmese prayer that expresses the spirit behind the offering of water: May He Be Cool as Water and Fresh as Flowers.

MAUNG HTIN AUNG is a distinguished scholar and university administrator as well as a foremost authority on Burmese folklore. Since 1963 he has been in the United States as a visiting professor, first at Columbia University and then at Wake Forest College. He has published a number of books on Burmese literature, religion and history and is the current president of the International Society of Asian Folklore.

HELEN G. TRAGER first went to Burma in 1951 as visiting professor at Rangoon University. Her husband, Frank Trager, was chief of the United States Economic Aid Program to Burma. The Tragers have since made seven trips to Burma and have adopted that country as their major field of interest. Mrs. Trager's doctoral thesis, *Burma Through Alien Eyes*, was published in 1966. Her article, *The Burmese Way with Children*, appeared in *Parents' Magazine*.

PAW OO THET was born in Mandalay where he began drawing at the age of fourteen and later studied with the grand old master of Mandalay, U Ba Thet. He also completed a correspondence course in the United States. Today Paw Oo Thet ranks as a leading Burmese artist. He lives in Rangoon where he is a member of a cooperative studio, but he frequently returns to Mandalay for vacations and for inspiration. He is married and the father of three children.